Best of Billy Joel Piano Solos

Allentown

Words and Music by Billy Joel

7

All About Soul

Words and Music by Billy Joel

And So It Goes

Words and Music by Billy Joel

And So It Goes

Words and Music by Billy Joel

Baby Grand

Words and Music by Billy Joel

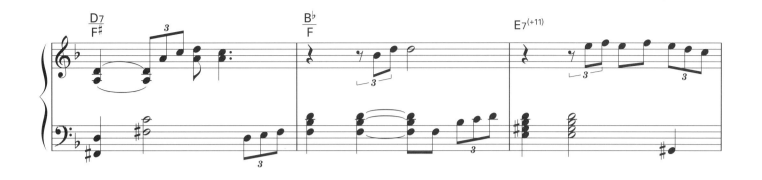

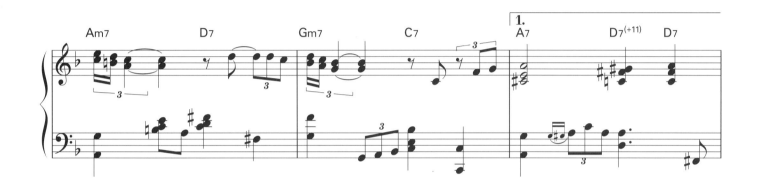

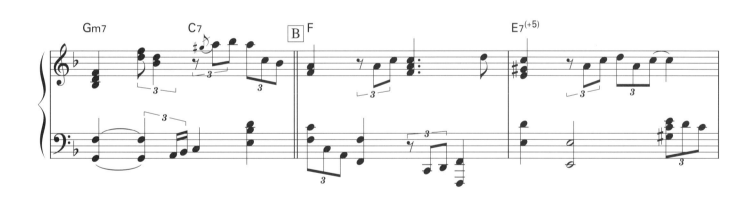

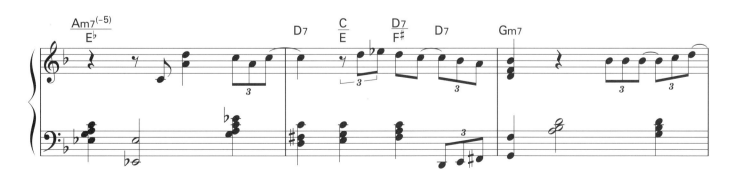

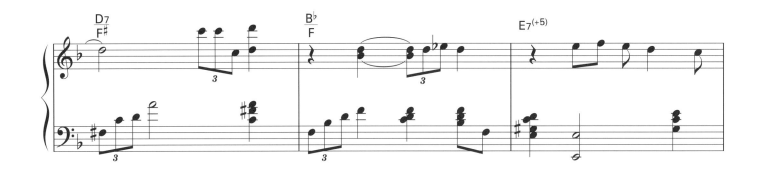

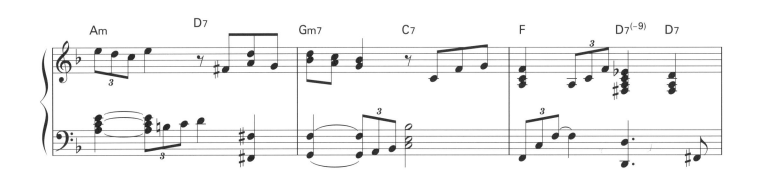

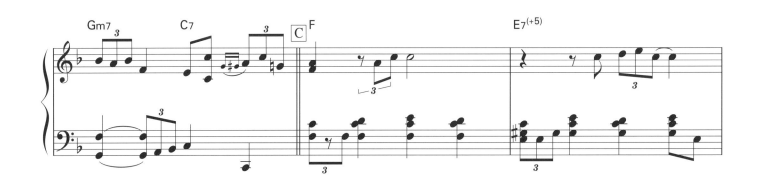

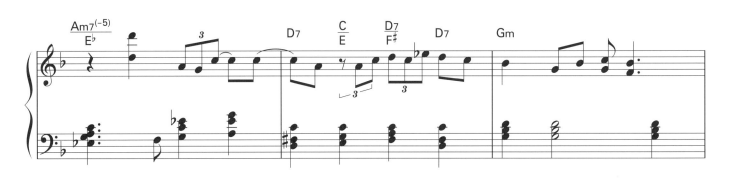

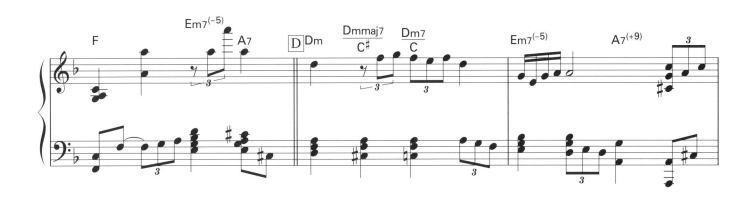

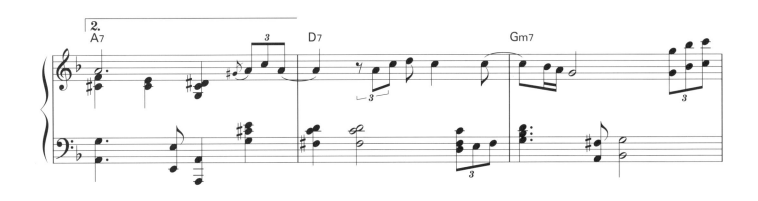

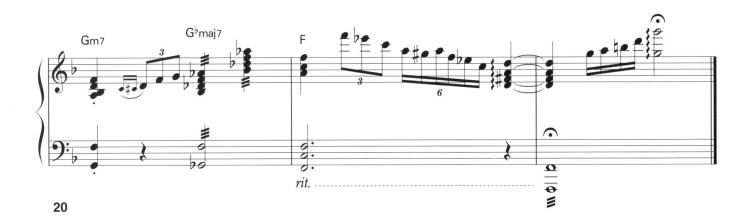

Honesty

Words and Music by Billy Joel

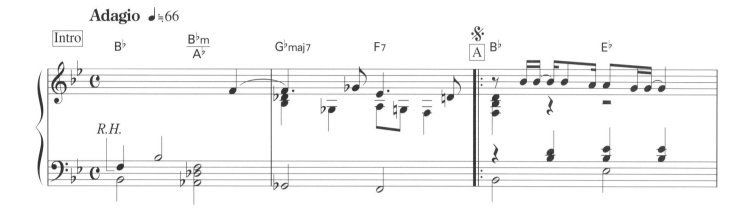

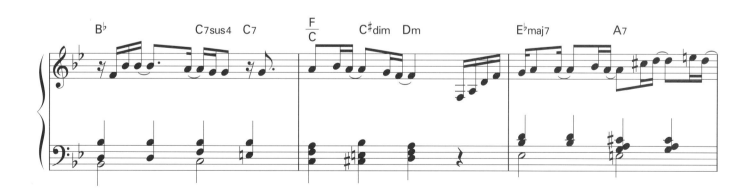

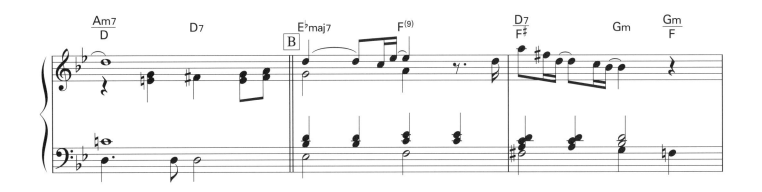

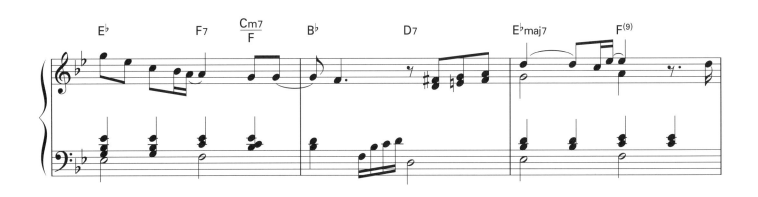

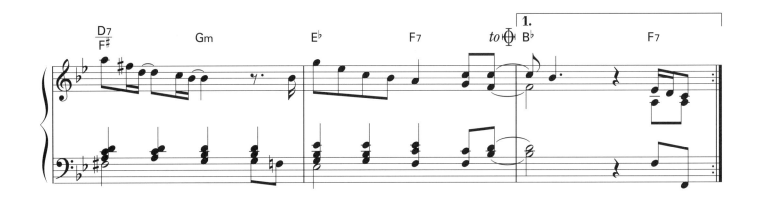

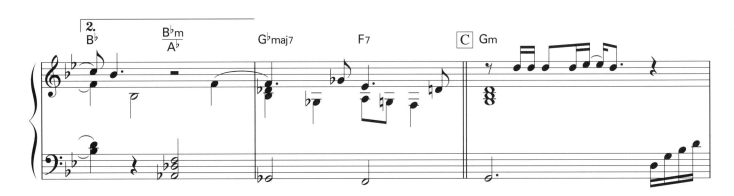

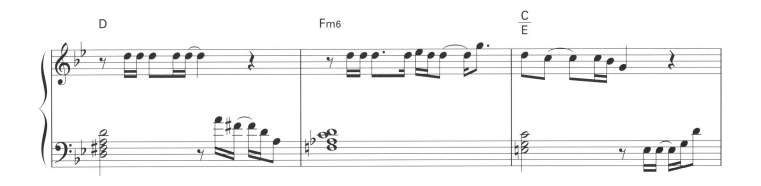

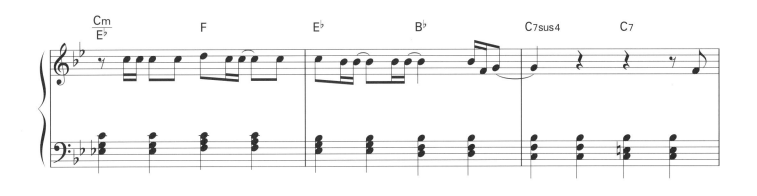

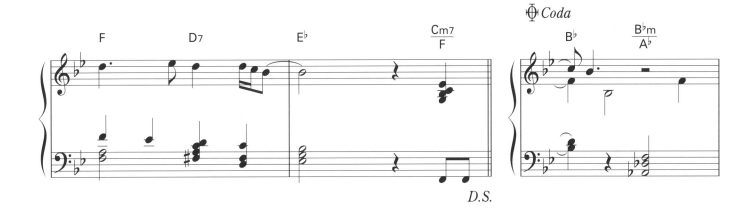

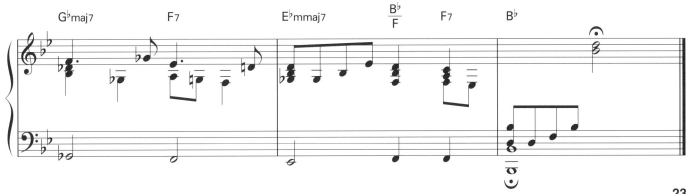

An Innocent Man

Words and Music by Billy Joel

It's Still Rock and Roll to Me

Words and Music by Billy Joel

Just the Way You Are

Words and Music by Billy Joel

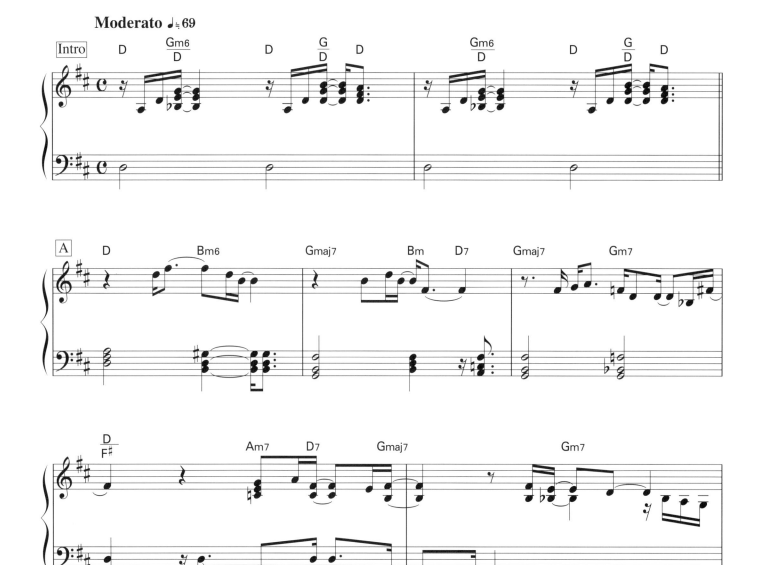

Piano Man

Words and Music by Billy Joel

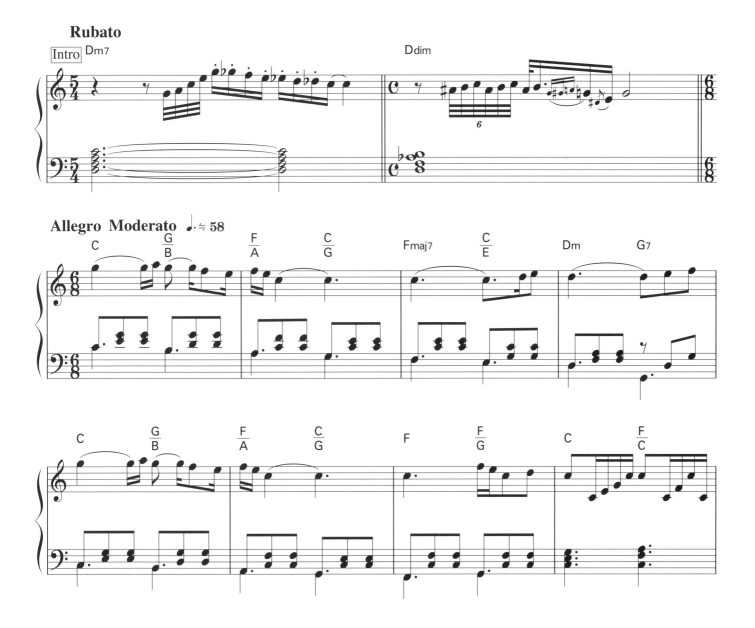

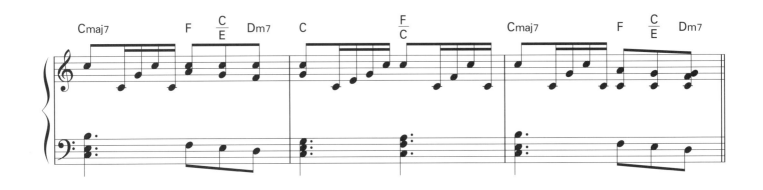

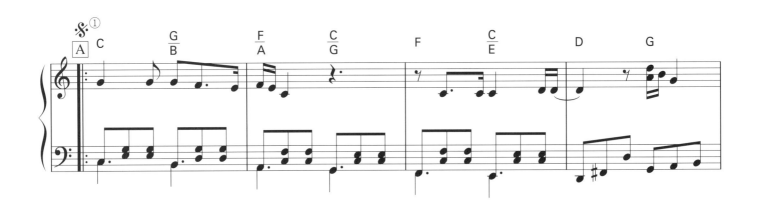

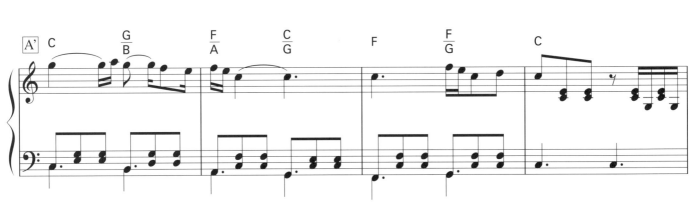

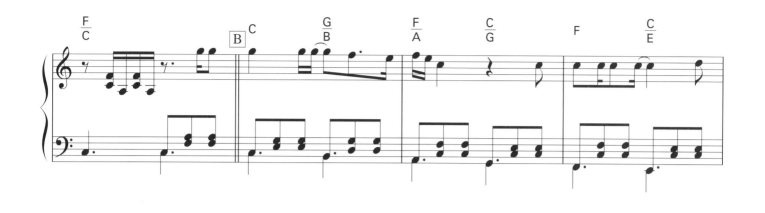

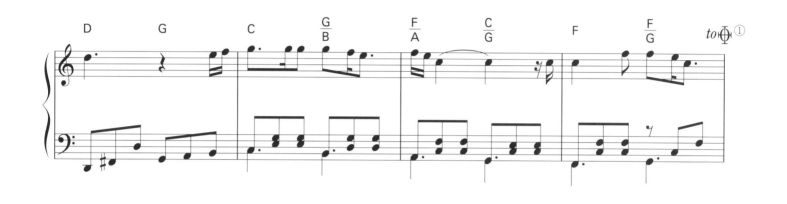

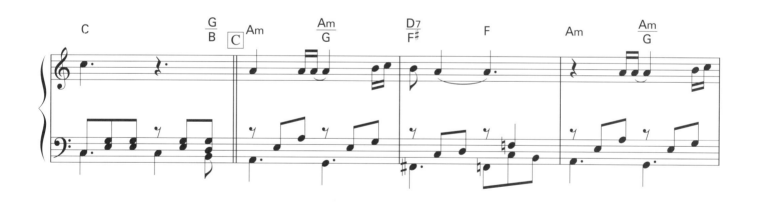

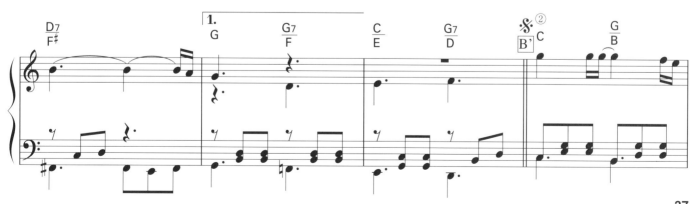

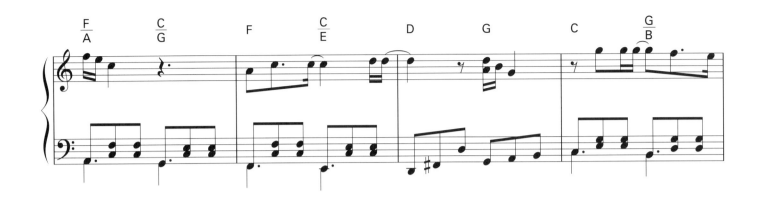

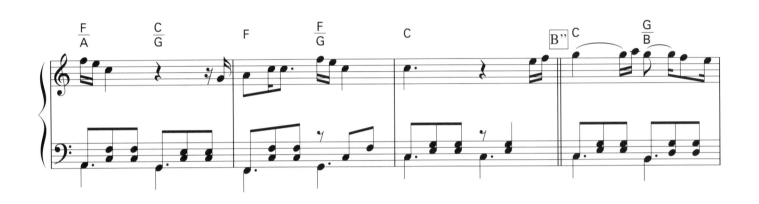

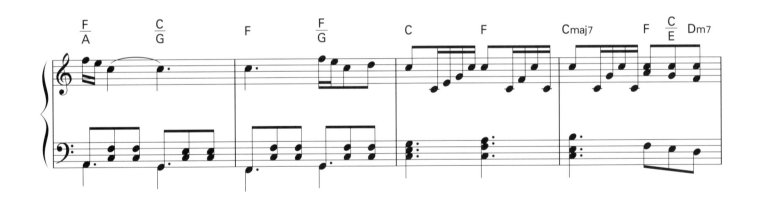

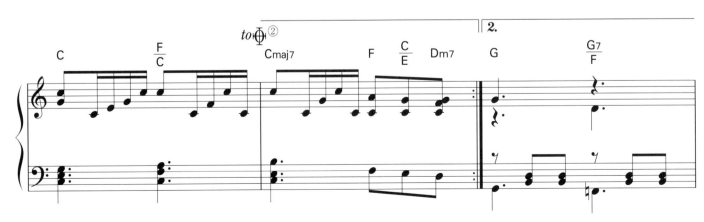

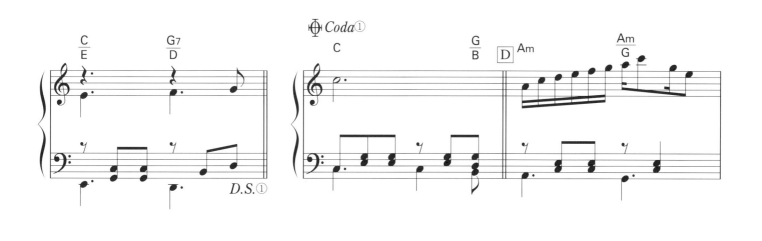

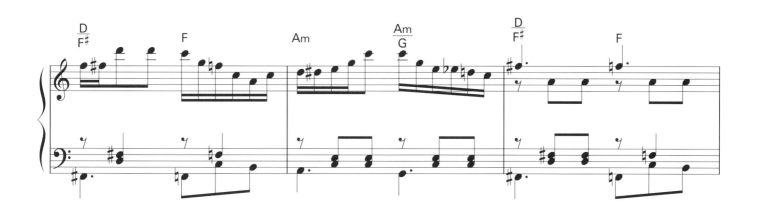

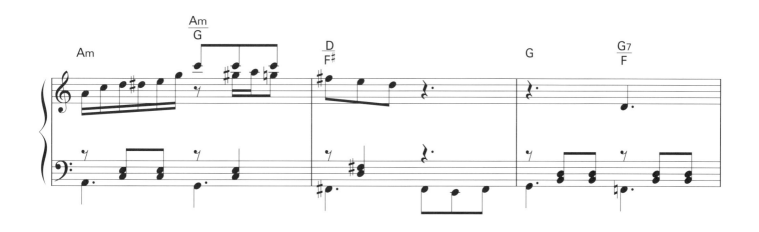

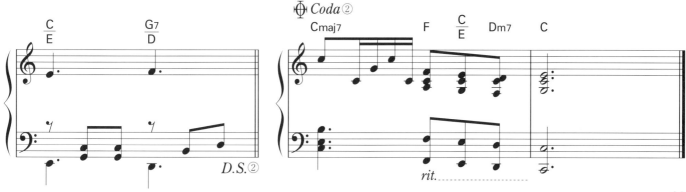

Keeping the Faith

Words and Music by Billy Joel

The Longest Time

Words and Music by Billy Joel

My Life

Words and Music by Billy Joel

Only the Good Die Young

Words and Music by Billy Joel

The River of Dreams

Words and Music by Billy Joel

She's Always a Woman

Words and Music by Billy Joel

Original Key : E♭

Allegro Moderato ♩. ≒ 58

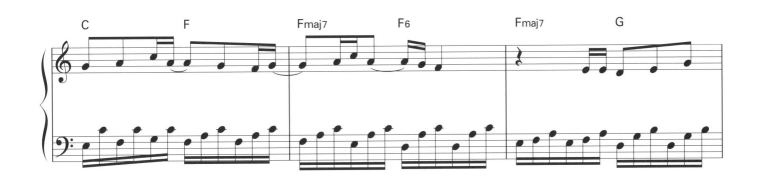

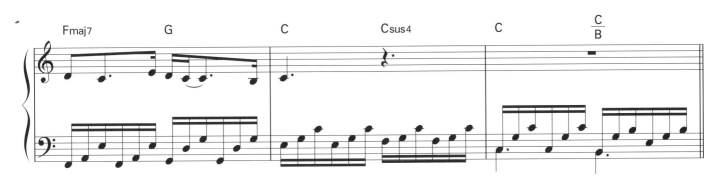

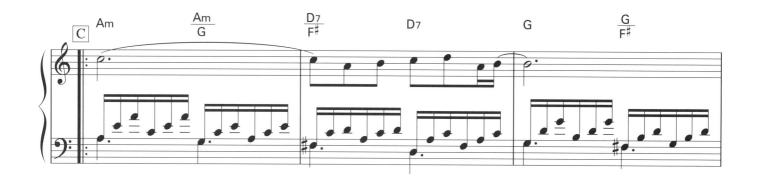

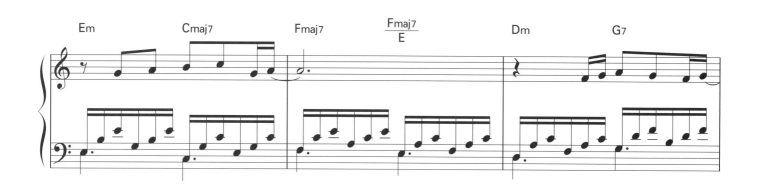

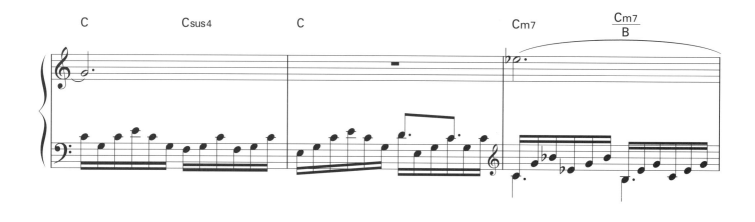

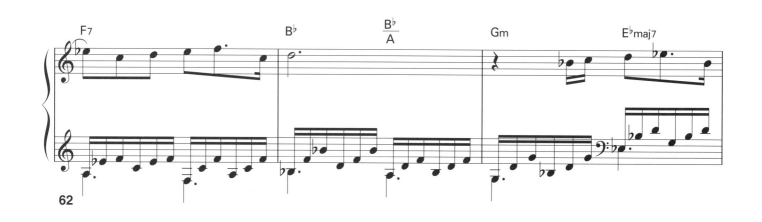

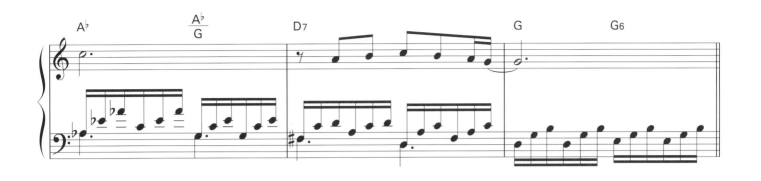

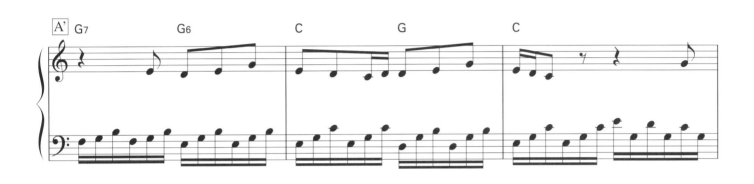

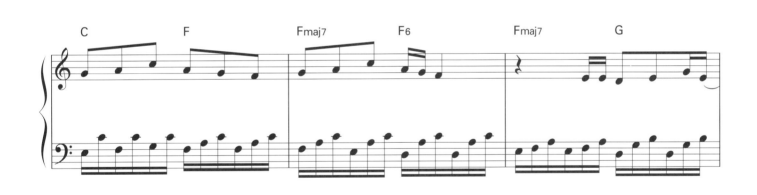

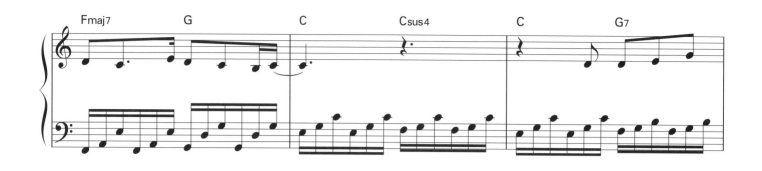

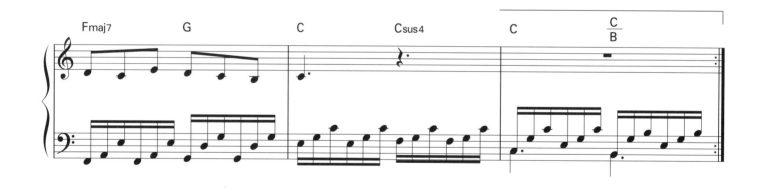

She's Got a Way

Words and Music by Billy Joel

Tell Her About It

Words and Music by Billy Joel

70

D.S.

We Didn't Start the Fire

Words and Music by Billy Joel

74

Uptown Girl

Words and Music by Billy Joel